First published November 2008

Published and distributed by
Affirmations Publishing House
34 Hyde Street, Bellingen NSW 2454 Australia
www.affirmations.com.au

Feathered Philosophers

illustrations by Kate Knapp

Design, text and illustrations by Kate Knapp

ISBN 978-0-9804060-2-3

10 9

Printed in China on recycled paper using vegetable based inks.

for

Mum and Dad
Samantha, Darren, Grace, Nettie
and my great love, Saffy.

Thanks to ...
My treasured friends and supporters.
The Affirmations family for taking my little birds by the wing into the open skies.
Dearest Glenda for the colourful title.
Alan James for your inspired, feathery words on the front, back and inside back covers.

It's not always black and white.

A colourful take on life's grey areas.

by
Kate Knapp

She told all her children
they could do anything
... it made them very light
and helped them fly

It's just not normal
bird behaviour

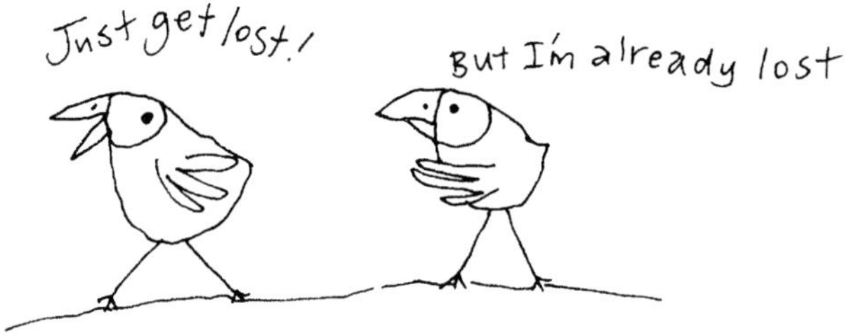
Just get lost!
But I'm already lost

When I turned fifty it
felt like I became invisible

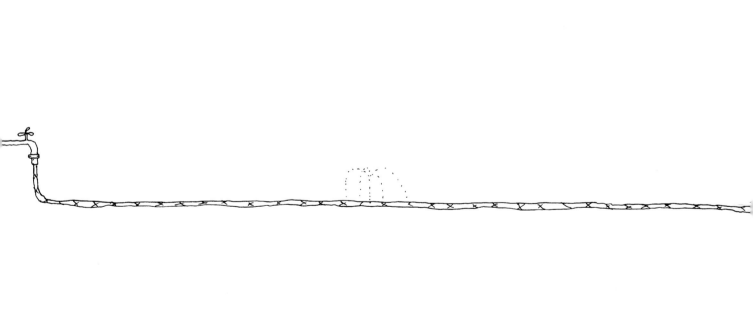

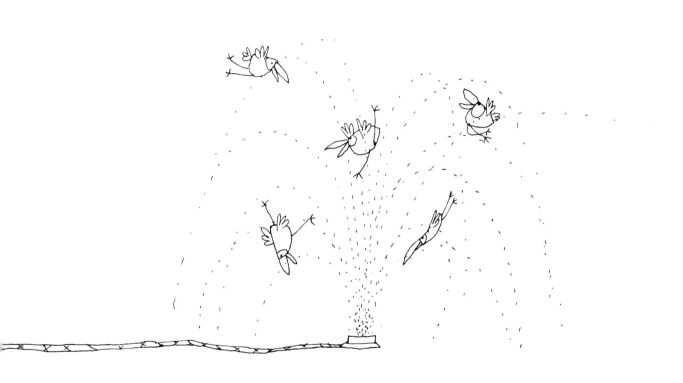

sprinkling silliness

You feel like home

I had a blood test and it seems I have high expectations. So I'm on a strict diet of no expecting and lots of enjoying.

my inner bird doesn't
feel like chirping today

I planted my pain in a
sunny spot in the garden.
A beautiful flower grew.

There's a bee in my hair and a gnat on my nose
I've eaten too many flowers and smell like a rose
There's too much nonsense in my head
I'm closing the doors and going to bed .

There she goes again

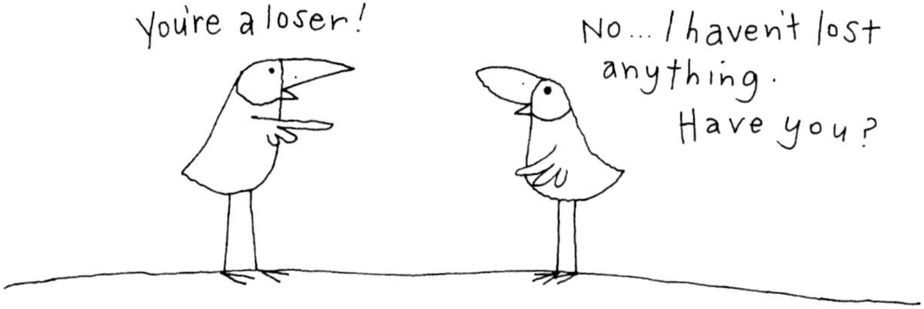
You're a loser!
No... I haven't lost anything. Have you?

in true love there
are no obstacles.

I decided to return all the expectations people had given me.

coming on a bit strong

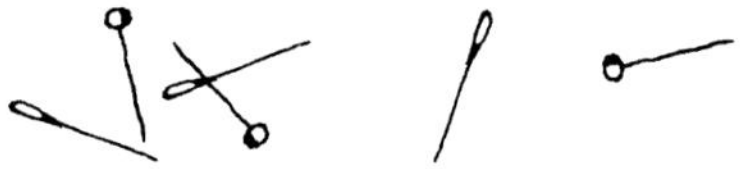

I'm sitting on a pear with a strawberry on my head,
The world looks better this way, or so I have read.
I think it's working, there's some tingling in my toes
Or is that pins and needles from sitting in this pose?

Why are you looking so sheepish?

One day I decided work was very
  overrated and simply walked away.
I was quite happy eating grass
  and common worms... and all
  my grey feathers disappeared.

exhaustion

innocence is a very rare thing
these days. If you find it
don't let it go.

thank you

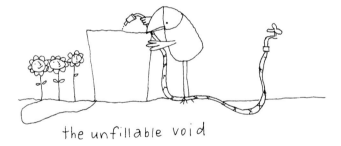

the unfillable void

Just as I think I've sorted life out...

Is there anyone out
there like me?

We're much stronger if we hold hands and become one.

I broke this one.... can I get
a replacement please.

please be well again

Y 0

disconnected

I am giving you a great gift,
it is the planet of life.
  Remember it is a part of you,
  it breathes with you, laughs
  with you, weeps with you and
  can stop living like you.
  Take it gently in your embrace
  and ask it what it needs and
  each night before sleep tell
   it you love it.

You know expectations have really
taken over. Once all anyone expected
was a little rain or perhaps someone
feathery to love.

thank goodness for idle chatter

You said if you won lotto you
wouldn't change a thing.

One particular day I decided guilt had
been a passenger on my journey for too
long. Besides it scratched the upholstery
with its sharp fingernails.

The next day I offered a ride to a far
nicer traveller called forgiveness who
always had fresh wildflowers that
made the car smell sweet.

her babies went out into
the world and she wept.

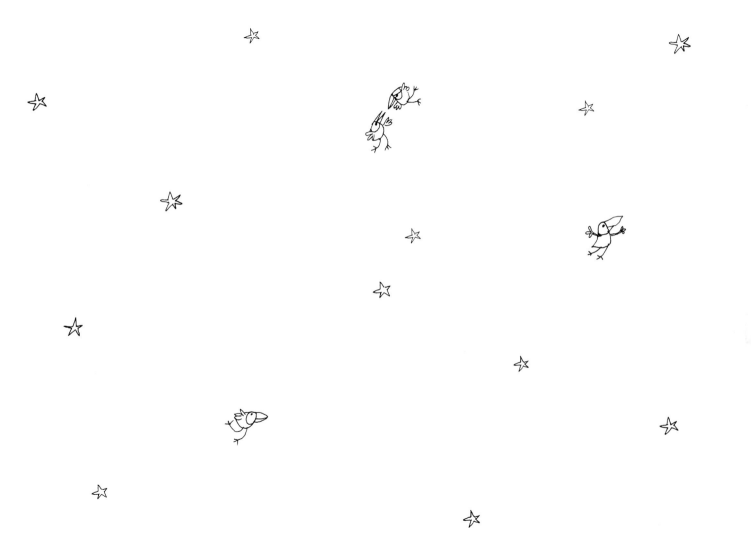

we were once
all very small

I'm really sorry

I'm far too emotional.
I'm way too fat.
I'm always this and seldom that.
But what do I care.
I don't give a fluff.
I'm totally fantastic and
believe none of that stuff!

I see you

darling just accept there
are parts of me you will
never understand

some things need protection

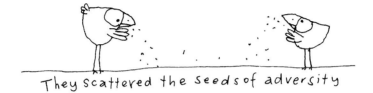

They scattered the seeds of adversity

and there grew flowers of freedom,
compassion and respect.

what's wrong with birds today?

well balanced birds

recharging

I change my mind so often
I exhaust myself.

amidst the destruction
in the world there was
a gentle warm breeze
that took her in its arms

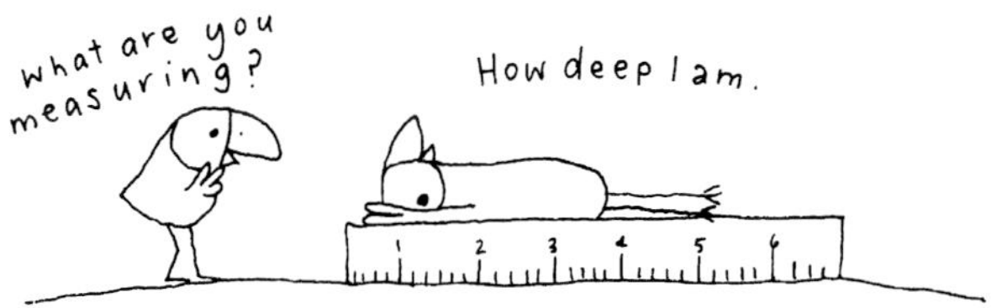
what are you measuring?
How deep I am.
1 2 3 4 5 6

Are you an insomniac?

I had an agreement with
depression. It had to make
a reservation 48 hours prior
to arriving. I always seem
to be fully booked.

They washed all the worries away with hot soapy water then dried them with an optimistic tea towel.

rest more

Catch me a fish, no make that two.
One for me and one for you.
We'll eat them together under the moon.
I'll sing salty songs whilst you play us a tune

What the hell did I do
with my centre?

I lost myself under an enormous pile of office stuff.

When I got out I found the nearest tree to sit in and let the breeze ruffle my feathers.

So you're Love . . . .
I thought you would
be far more beautiful...
and wear nicer clothes.

she clutched her crumpled
trampled heart and wept
because she so foolishly
gave it away.

Sometimes she would launch
into rude songs ... it was
very embarrassing.

embellished stories

You're really not very grounded

Lots of people had lent me their opinions.
They were interesting at first but then
became quite noisy and intrusive and
frankly rather dull.

So I baked a big cherry cake (good for quietening opinions), gave them a huge slice each and sent them back to their owners. I was ever wary of taking others' opinions.

You're very ordinary
but extremely beautiful

I love you but I
don't really understand you

I think you've
gone too far!

Yes...it's fantastic!

When I confronted my fear
it just exploded into a jug
of very sunny flowers.

please don't walk away

Follow your heart

I'm so confused all I
can do is sit very still
and hope it passes.

wonder what it's
like being a
high flyer?

My feathers turn to
lead when we're apart.

It's for your own good!

I am richer in one moment
with my friends than I would
be with all the money in the world.

saying I love you becomes easier with practice.

some days look like this . . .

and other days!

the perfection of imperfection

I'm not going mad, it's just no one
has ever heard me tell the truth before.

optimism is a great companion

My worries had totally tried to take over. So I went to the beach, packed them in a boat and sent them to sea.

Later I heard they ended up on a tropical island where there was no such things as worries. So by day they picked pineapples and at night danced in the moonlight.

For a moment she loved
all parts of herself.
It made her feel enormous.

I can't wait for mess to
come back in fashion.
Zen is such hard work
and a bit cold.

Tell me what you need to grow?

Oh just a bit of water and sunshine...

but most importantly... love.

problems solved together
on the park bench.

He fitted just perfectly
in her handbag

I've never heard of resentment...
it doesn't sound like a bird word.

But grandfather you're losing all your feathers!

Not losing but giving back to the earth my seeds
of wisdom and memories for all the
wonder it gave to me.

God I'm sorry

I nestled into the tree
trunk and pressed my
ear very close and when
the wind stopped and all
was still and quiet I
heard the tree's heartbeat.
I knew then I was safe.

couldn't the whole world
hear the almighty sound
of my heart breaking?

I don't quite fit in.

Sometimes he would just go very
   high into a tree and ponder stuff.
She had great difficulty just
       leaving him there.

I don't care what kind
of a bird you are...
What job do you do?

Life had begun to look like the inside of a shopping centre
... as far as the eye could see everything was artificial.

chasing her missing sparkle

She's a little bit flighty.
If I let go...goodness
knows where she'll end up.

compassionate tears
are food for the earth.

making someone smaller
does not make you bigger.

don't you drop me!

I'm like concentrated laundry detergent:
very strong!

She made cups of
tea that washed
all the worries away

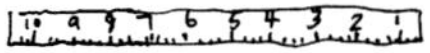

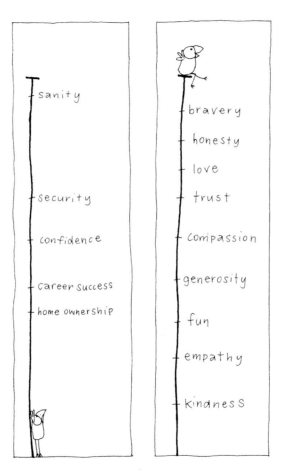

sanity

security

confidence

career success
home ownership

bravery

honesty

love

trust

compassion

generosity

fun

empathy

kindness

m e a s u r i n g   u p

I am with you always

She cradled the
moon to sleep.

everyone's so scared of carbs these days.
dinner rolls are getting awful low self esteem.
So when I go to lunches, my compassionate
side feels the need to eat them all.
   Butter too! It's got rejection issues.

God it gets bad down here sometimes

I saw your grief and loss.
There was nothing I could
do but feel a tiny bit of
it with you.

some of the biggest
moments in life
are the tiniest.

Today, thinking is like
Knitting with Knotty wool.

Wondering what age they leave the nest.

The sky is pink the moon is blue
My heart is a nest and there's room
for you too.

I had these breathtaking
spells of panic like I
had been locked in a jar.

What's so good about words?
Try chirping!

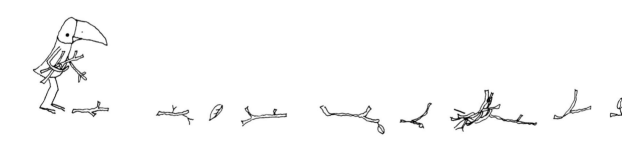

unnatural disaster

praying for simplicity

Kate and her studio Twigseeds are well known for their
playful, insightful greeting cards and art prints. The Twigseeds nest
has hatched a flock of feathered and furry philosophers who inspire us to
"consider our world".

Kate divides her time between Brisbane and the
Sunshine Coast hinterland in Australia. This is her first book.

To find out more about Kate and the Twigseeds family, please visit
www.twigseeds.com